Five fancy fish can swim

5

# Five fancy fish can play football...

## and have fun in a fort.

They can eat **f**ine **f**ood.
It tastes so **f**abulous!

# Five fancy fish can wave their fins at a friend!